Department of the Environment

Procedural Manual Evaluative Framework

(Version 1)

Assessment of Alternative Colliery Spoil Disposal Options

June 1986

London   Her Majesty's Stationery Office.

CONTENTS

1.0 INTRODUCTION

The Evaluative Framework is designed to assist decision making in relation to future disposal schemes for deep mined colliery spoil. It encourages the systematic investigation of a range of alternative schemes in order to compare the advantages and disadvantages of each option against various economic and environmental factors. The Evaluative Framework has been designed for use during the stage leading to the submission of a planning application by the National Coal Board (now known as British Coal) to the Mineral Planning Authority (MPA). It may also assist decisions about the best source of fill material for large scale reclamation sites.

The need for improved decision making was raised by the Commission on Energy and the Environment (the Flowers Commission) in 1981. The Framework presented here results from a two year research project commissioned by the Department of the Environment from Ove Arup and Partners. During this period the Evaluative Framework has been compiled and tested on a series of case studies and refined into its current form. This work has been undertaken in consultation with the National Coal Board (NCB) and Local Authorities in the Yorkshire, Nottinghamshire, Derbyshire coalfield area. There is a continuing need to monitor the use of the Framework in practice and to refine it further over time.

It is intended that this Evaluative Framework should be a flexible tool used to assist decision making. In applying the Framework to assess options for colliery spoil disposal it is important that a commonsense approach is taken. Bearing in mind that the Framework has to cater for a very wide range of options both in scale and complexity, the users should not apply the Framework rigidly, but be prepared, in joint agreement, to omit, simplify or vary sections of the Framework to suit the particular options under consideration.

2.0 DESCRIPTION OF THE EVALUATIVE FRAMEWORK

This chapter describes in outline the form and content of the Evaluative Framework. The Evaluative Framework is illustrated on the next page, and is contained in this Manual.

The Evaluative Framework comprises 3 phases :-

Phase I	–	Selection of Options
Phase II	–	Economic Assessment
	–	Environmental Assessment
Phase III	–	Combined Evaluation

The Framework is extensive and for each spoil disposal option covers separately the economic and environmental factors. In its application it has been designed to encompass spoil disposal schemes which can range from a tip extension to a full new coalfield development. The Evaluative Framework is also comprehensive in that it provides for a full range of current handling, transport and disposal options.

The first two phases incorporate questionnaires which can be completed quickly and which lead to the identification and quantification of the relevant factors. Phase III of the Evaluative Framework brings together the economic costs and the environmental impacts to help the user to determine the preferred option for spoil disposal.

EVALUATIVE FRAMEWORK

PHASE I
Selection of options

PHASE II
Costs and impacts

PHASE III
Combined evaluation

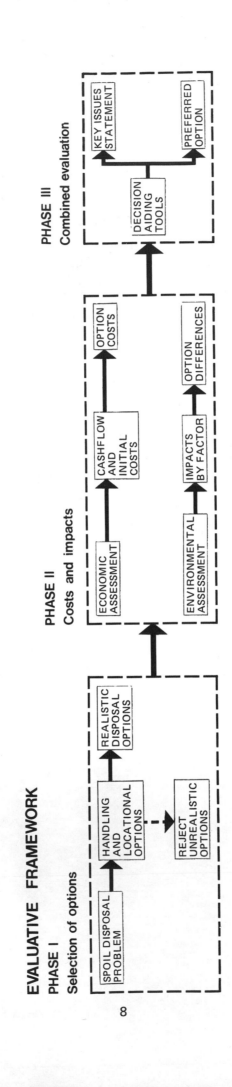

- SPOIL DISPOSAL PROBLEM
- HANDLING AND LOCATIONAL OPTIONS
- REJECT UNREALISTIC OPTIONS
- REALISTIC DISPOSAL OPTIONS
- ECONOMIC ASSESSMENT
- CASHFLOW AND INITIAL COSTS
- OPTION COSTS
- ENVIRONMENTAL ASSESSMENT
- IMPACTS BY FACTOR
- OPTION DIFFERENCES
- DECISION AIDING TOOLS
- KEY ISSUES STATEMENT
- PREFERRED OPTION

8

2.0 cont'd

The purpose of Phase I is to identify all realistic options for disposal of spoil from a particular colliery or development. It is therefore site specific and requires the NCB to provide information where it exists on current activity and to make available forecasts of future spoil make. The MPA or MPAs may be able to help identify disposal locations and give guidance on planning constraints.

Phase II will take forward the limited number of realistic options and for each will separately examine defined economic and environmental issues. Where possible, all costs and factors will be quantified using separate indicators.

Phase III brings together the economic and environmental aspects in a judgemental process. It is recognised that this area might give rise to differences of opinion between the parties. This will largely arise from the different emphasis each party might wish to attach to the economic costs and the various environmental factors. In order to smooth progress on this issue Phase III provides two decision aiding tools which are intended to assist decision making by identifying the critical issues upon which subsequent negotiations can focus.

3.0 SUGGESTED WORKING ARRANGEMENTS

The Evaluative Framework is designed to assist decision making in two main situations:

- during local planning in response to the disposal needs of a particular colliery, and

- to identify appropriate sources of spoil for large scale reclamation projects.

In respect of the former, the Framework encourages the identification and evaluation of alternative disposal options for a colliery or group of collieries. It is intended that the NCB should apply the procedure when it is formulating ideas for particular collieries. The Framework should not be used after a decision on a disposal option has been made, nor should it be used by the NCB solely as a way of justifying a pre-determined scheme.

Within limits of confidentiality the application of the Evaluative Framework should be undertaken as a co-operative approach between the NCB and MPA encouraging input from other interested parties such as the Ministry of Agriculture, Fisheries and Food (MAFF) and the Water Authorities, at specified stages in the process. Precise arrangements will have to be worked out between the parties at local level, depending on the strength of current liaison arrangements.

In general, the parties will initially find it useful to select jointly the options to be investigated and to agree the level of detail of the subsequent analyses appropriate to the problem in hand. The costings information might then generally be assembled by the NCB, while some of the environmental information could more easily be provided by the MPA. The techniques included in the combined evaluation stage are designed to assist the choice of a preferred option.

3.0 cont'd

Upon completion of the Framework the NCB will separately decide whether or not it proceeds to the submission of a formal planning application for a particular scheme. It will then be the responsibility of the MPA to respond to that application, taking account of the recommendation of its Officers. If planning permission is refused the Department of the Environment holds the ultimate power of determination of the application through appeals to the Secretary of State.

Some of the information provided by the NCB for the detailed economic analysis of options may be regarded as commercially sensitive. In these circumstances the amount of detail that can be disclosed will be a matter for discretion by the particular NCB Area. In this situation, a summary report of the Evaluative Framework results could accompany formal submission of the planning application to the MPA.

At the wider level the Framework is intended to assist the formulation of broad options for disposal; for example testing the viability of transporting spoil from one or more collieries to a remote reception site. The initiative for such schemes is perhaps more likely to come from MPAs at a sub-regional or regional level or from joint working parties of different interests. The NCB may also find it useful to use the Framework at Area level to test the effects of concentration schemes, and to assess options for new coalfield developments.

If agreement cannot be reached between the NCB and MPA to a joint working approach, the Evaluative Framework has been designed to facilitate its completion by any independent party. Professional advice on the estimation of costs from a quantity surveyor or engineer would generally be required.

4.0 PROCEDURAL NOTES

4.1 Background

The Evaluative Framework consists of three phases:

Phase I   Selection of Options

Phase II Economic Assessment

           Environmental Assessment

Phase III Combined Evaluation.

The first two phases are in the form of questionnaires with interim summaries. The economic assessment procedure can be completed manually, although a computer routine is available. Phase I and the environmental assessment procedure may be set up by the user on a word processing package if the Framework is to be in frequent use.

Phase III comprises two decision aiding tools which may be used during negotiations as appropriate.

The following sections give general notes to assist the completion of each of the phases of the Evaluative Framework. Detailed notes on individual questions appear on the facing pages in the Framework.

The Framework is oriented to evaluating between alternative disposal sites. It can also however be used to test for the most suitable originating colliery or collieries to reclaim a particular reception site. There is an alternative format of the Phase I questionnaire for this application, which can be found in Annex 1 together with guidance notes on the other parts of the Framework.

4.2 Phase I – Selection of Options
General

Phase I is in the form of a series of questions which provide background information to the exercise. It focuses initially on details of the colliery (or groups of collieries) in question and the required tipping capacity for spoil disposal. It then identifies areas of land which either singly or in combination could satisfy the tipping volume requirement.

In selecting such options, attention is given not just to land in the vicinity already owned by the NCB, but also to sites with opportunities for environmental gain. Options for disposal are then subjected to preliminary testing in order to disregard unrealistic ones. Preliminary design and costings work is then required for each of the feasible options as a basis for the more detailed later analyses in Phase II. The number of options to be taken forward into Phase II would normally be between 2 and 6, depending on circumstances. If the NCB and MPA are agreed on a preferred site or combination of sites at the end of Phase I, they may jointly opt to by-pass the detailed comparative analyses in Phase II. In doing so they should take into account any views to the contrary from any of the other interested parties such as MAFF or Water Authorities who have been consulted during Phase I. Within an option there may still be alternative ways of working the site(s) and alternative methods of ameliorating the level of impact which the two parties should evaluate. Sections of the Phase II Framework assist in this process.

4.3 Phase II – Economic Assessment
General

The objective of this phase is to identify the difference in costs between options not to define the absolute costs of tipping for any particular option.

4.3 cont'd

There is a need to define clearly the following parameters before starting to assemble costs:

- start date of tipping scheme;

- end date of analysis (this should generally be around 20 years from the start date, or the life of the scheme if less than 20 years, see Phase I notes);

- time horizon of costs relating to that scheme (this may extend a few years before the start date to include advance site purchase and preparation costs where significant, and after the end date of tipping to include restoration and aftercare costs). It is less critical to spread costs after the end of tipping as these have less effect on the Net Present Cost and are in any case small when a progressive restoration scheme is in operation. Year 1 should be taken as the first year of spending on any option. This is then taken as the base for all the other options. Discounting is then carried out back to Year 0 i.e. the previous year;

- start point of disposal process for measuring costs (this would generally be as the spoil leaves the coal preparation plant);

- date at which prices are quoted (this would generally be the current year and should be stated at the commencement of the questionnaire);

- whether calendar or NCB financial years are to be considered (usually the latter).

The criteria for inclusion of costs should be whether the particular item affects the decision between options or, in the case of one option, whether to go ahead or not. (The cost of fines treatment, for example, would normally only be included where different options involved different levels of use of treatment and lagoons.)

There should be no double counting of costs. This may arise, for example, in relation to initial costs if hire charges are taken as a proxy for operating costs for surface mobile plant without removing the depreciation element and other financing costs normally included in NCB hire rates.

4.3 cont'd

There should be no inclusion of initial costs which have been incurred in cash terms at some previous date in relation to another scheme i.e. no "sunk costs". However, if an option allows NCB to dispose of land or plant the sale proceeds are included, as is any residual value of equipment that could be transferred to another scheme at the end of tipping.

Cost Analysis by Activity

This is in the form of a series of sequential questions designed to resolve two principal issues:-

- what are the resource inputs required for each alternative?

- how much does each input cost?

The questionnaire has three columns. Each question requires at least two responses, as follows:-

Initial/
Recurring: For items whose classification is unambiguous, no action required. For items which could be either, indicate which classification applies.

Cost: Give an estimate of the cost of the relevant item at current values. Give total cost for capital items, and annual cost for profit and loss account items.

Comments: The following is mandatory:-
i] the year or years in which the expenditure is incurred.

The following are required only where relevant:-

i]   the life of capital assets where this is less than the period over which the analysis is conducted;

ii]   any anticipated changes in operating costs in real terms (e.g. increasing maintenance in later years);

iii]   any other relevant comments.

Most questions on annual operating costs require a summation of sub-categories to be carried out before a complete answer can be given.   In terms of NCB accounting categories, these would typically include labour, materials, repairs, maintenance, heat, light, power and any other direct costs.   It may be necessary to adopt a bills of quantity type approach to costing each item.   This level of detail is generally not required to be presented as part of the Evaluative Framework although, in the event of disputes between the major parties, more detailed costings for certain items might need to be revealed.

The economic assessment is designed to evaluate options on a cashflow basis, rather than by internal accounting charges.   In general, therefore, the use of plant pool rates is discouraged in favour of actual capital and profit and loss account expenditure.

This approach should apply to all equipment solely or mainly used in disposal.   It is accepted, however, that occasional use of plant cannot be represented in this manner and so plant pool rates should apply in these cases.   Wherever plant pool rates are used, this fact should be noted in the Comments column.

4.3   cont'd

In completing the questions it is fundamental to avoid double counting. Cost items that are difficult to sub-divide should therefore be entered under the main activity headings. For example, the labour costs (wage costs and wage charges in NCB's terms) of the Site Superintendent should generally be entered under

Placement and Compaction during the years of tipping operations even though his duties may include overseeing the conveyor and lagoons. This fact should then be noted in the Comments column. Where NCB already owns an asset that is to be reused in an option, only marginal costs such as the expense of moving the asset or refurbishing it should be included. If the asset is not required but can be transferred to another part of NCB's operations, the disposal proceeds can be offset against that option.

For those options relating to off-site tipping locations, questions under some activity headings, such as site preparation and handling and transport, cover costs incurred at both the colliery and the reception site.

Summary of Costs

This summarises the costs for each option. There are four distinct sub-stages.

i]   Cashflow Summary. The activity costs are assigned to specific years on an overall Cashflow Summary sheet. The flows for each year are then totalled.

ii]   Net Present Cost. The Net Present Cost is then calculated on the Cashflow Summary Sheet by discounting back to year 0 each annual cashflow by the appropriate factor, based on an annual rate of 5%.

4.3   cont'd

iii]   Equivalent Annual Cost.   The Equivalent Annual Cost is
       calculated on the Cashflow Summary Sheet using the formula:-

$$EAC = \frac{(1 + i)^a \times NPC \times i}{1 - \dfrac{1}{(1 + i)^n}}$$

where   EAC = Equivalent Annual Cost

             NPC = Net Present Cost

             a   = number of years before tipping
                   commences

             i   = annual discount rate (5%)

             n = number of years of tipping.

The EAC is then converted to a cost per cubic metre or per
tonne by dividing by the average production of spoil to be
disposed of each year.   Separate calculations can be made for
each activity heading.

In strict theory, the EAC itself should be developed on a per
cubic metre or per tonne of spoil basis.   The above formula
is in fact a subset of a more complex formula whose derivation
is shown in Annex 2.   It is valid only in cases where the
annual production tipped is constant but is significantly
easier to calculate manually than the full formula.

iv]   Initial Cost.   The advance capital costs up to and including
      the first year of tipping is calculated by abstracting the
      relevant information from the questionnaire and transferring it
      to the Initial Cost Summary Sheet.

Whatever the cashflow stream of a project and, whatever the
discounted Net Present Cost, it is always possible to calculate
a constant cashflow stream which will give rise to the same
Net Present Cost.   The constant annual cashflow which is
calculated is called the Equivalent Annual Cost.

4.3   cont'd

Calculation of the Equivalent Annual Cost is straightforward. As an example, consider a project with the following cashflows at to-day's prices where tipping starts in year 2:-

	Year 1	Year 2	Year 3	Year 4	Year 5	Year 6	TOTAL
Initial	1000			150			1150
Recurring		250	250	250	250	250	1250
TOTAL COSTS	1000	250	250	400	250	250	2400
Discounted at 5% p.a.	952	227	216	329	196	187	2107

The cost of the scheme at today's prices spread over 6 years is £2400. The Net Present Cost at 5% is £2107.

Using the formula the Equivalent Annual Cost is :-

$$EAC = (1 + 0.05)^1 \times \frac{£2107 \times 0.05}{1 - \dfrac{1}{(1 + 0.05)^5}}$$

$$= £511$$

This can be shown to give the same Net Present Cost, i.e.

	Year 1	Year 2	Year 3	Year 4	Year 5	Year 6	TOTAL
Equivalent Annual Cost	0	511	511	511	511	511	
Discounted at 5% p.a.	0	464	442	420	401	382	2109

In analytical terms, therefore, the actual cashflow for the project gives rise to the same end result as that from an even cashflow of £511 per year while tipping takes place. £511 can therefore be expressed as the Equivalent Annual Cost of the project cashflow. Had there been no significant advance capital costs before tipping commenced then the first component of the EAC formula would not have been used because 'a' would have been equal to 0 and $(1 + i)^a$ would have become 1.

4.3 cont'd

Comparison of Option Costs

The end result of Phase II Economic is three sets of key indicators for each option, namely:

1] The Equivalent Annual Cost per cubic metre or tonne of spoil disposed together with the EAC per activity heading. The latter represents a proportioning in accordance with the total cashflow.

2] The Cashflow Total as an indication of the overall scale of resources required.

3] The Initial Cost up to the first year of tipping.

The overall EAC and the Initial Cost are economic criteria carried forward into Phase III; the EAC by activity and the cashflow total are purely indicative.

4.4 Phase II - Environmental Assessment
General

The details of the spoil disposal option will have been prepared at the outcome of Phase I, Question 5.2. Additional details of the site works, profiles and screening features may be shown at greater detail than 1:10,000 scale where appropriate.

The initial task for the environmental assessment involves the definition of the study area within which to assess the existing conditions and likely impact of the options under consideration. On maps of either 1:25,000 scale or 1:10,000 scale it is necessary to draw the approximate boundaries of the area from which the proposed site and scheme will be either visible or be affected in some way such as extra noise disturbance, diversion or closure of routes or loss of amenity.

4.4   cont'd

The environmental appraisal of each option entails both an assessment of the existing environmental quality of the proposed site with its surroundings and the impact which could be expected from each option.   Different methods of working and scale of ameliorative measures may influence the expected impact of a given site.   The exercise involves mainly desk-top work although site investigations will supplement the information derived from maps, plans and reports.   Photographic records of the site are of considerable benefit for information and display of impacts.

Assessment of Environmental Impacts

This consists of a series of questions which are grouped under different headings.   The questionnaire has been designed for answers to be given alongside each question on the form.   Many of the questions seek information in two parts, one relating to the site itself and the other to the surroundings.   Likely data sources are described in the guidance notes.

Summary Tables of Environmental Impacts

This stage consists of a set of summary tables in which the environmental impacts of an option can be summarised.   Each table includes three columns to indicate the timing of the anticipated impact during the tipping scheme, the scale of features affected and the different parties affected.   Environmental factors, grouped into four main headings, are listed down the left hand axis of the tables.   The transport route section only needs completion for off-site options.

4.4 cont'd

Summary of Option Differences

This consists of a single table in which the differences in terms of environmental impacts between the options being assessed can be stated. To assist the evaluations in Phase III, the final columns of this table note whether differences between options are significant and if so, which option is least affected and which worst affected by each environmental factor. The conclusions from this table can then be taken forward for evaluation in Phase III.

4.5 Phase III - Combined Evaluation

The aim of Phase III is to present information on options in a manageable form to assist decision making. The method compares the outputs from Phase II Economic (which are definitive) with the outputs from Phase II Environmental (which are more subjective). Two decision aiding tools are presented to help identify the critical issues upon which subsequent negotiations can focus.

The output from the economic assessment will be monetary units in terms of Equivalent Annual Cost per cubic metre or per tonne of spoil and initial cost for each option. Thus not only will there be an implied ranking for the options but the relative differences between the options will also have been established.

The output from the environmental assessment has up to this Phase, been measured in different units (or in some cases may only be in descriptive form). Thus, although it is possible to rank the options on each factor by giving preference to those with least impact, there is often no easy and objective way to select the best option on overall environmental grounds.

Before proceeding to the combination of the economic costs and environmental factors, Phase III invites the user to complete an opening statement identifying the key environmental factors in terms of comparing the particular set of options under consideration. This simplifies the issues to be tested using the decision aiding tools.

4.5 cont'd

The first of the decision aiding tools provides a sieving technique and it is recommended as a starting point. The second technique provides a more detailed approach to comparing options on a factor by factor basis taking two options at a time.

A : Option Rankings

This requires the user to indicate his preferences graphically by allocating stars between options on each economic and environmental factor. One star is given to the worst option, five to the best with the remainder within this range according to relative performance. Columns are then compared and if there is one option with a low incidence of stars it might be possible to eliminate it. On the other hand it might be that a dominant option might emerge to the satisfaction of all parties (indicated by a high incidence of stars). This is unlikely often to be the case since if a jointly preferred option had emerged at the end of Phase I the parties are likely to have by-passed subsequent Phases of the Evaluative Framework and would have proceeded to detailed design.

B : Pairwise Comparison

This method compares two options chosen at random. For each factor the better option is chosen and the reasons noted. Then by comparison of all the factors the better option can be identified and the worse option discarded. A further option is then compared with that remaining from the first test and the process of successive elimination continues until the preferred option remains. The preferred option should then be tested against the first option that was dismissed to ensure conformity of choice.

If in comparing options, the preferred choice is not clear cut and raises a difficult trade-off, that pairing can be left unresolved and each can be compared against the next option. At the end of the exercise there may need to be some reiteration to check that all options not eliminated have been paired against each other.

4.5   B : cont'd

An alternative way of proceeding is to start with the least cost option and consider in turn and comment upon each environmental factor.   Again the worse overall option is discarded.   The next least expensive scheme could then be taken and its environmental effects compared with those of the lesser cost scheme.   In this way a direct relationship could be established on an iterative basis for each option on each aspect.   A third way would be to take the best environmental option first and to compare it successively with other options.

Completion of the Evaluative Framework

Finally, the users are required to complete a Key Issues Statement.   In cases where a preferred option emerges this may mean briefly stating the reasons for this choice with reference to the main environmental effects identified from the Framework and to justify this choice against the economic costs.

In other cases the Statement should summarise the key trade-offs that need to be resolved by subsequent decision makers in selecting the preferred option.

For guidance worked examples of the summary sheets for the Phase II Economic and Environmental Assessment, together with a full example of the Phase III techniques are included in Annex 3.   The tables reflect one of the case studies used in the Ove Arup and Partners research study and are based on published data sources.

GLOSSARY

Aftercare Maintenance of the tip after initial restoration to return the soil to good agricultural condition. Includes seeding, planting, cultivating, fertilising, watering and draining.

Aggregate Broken stone, slag, gravel, sand or similar inert material which forms a substantial part of concretes, asphalts or roads.

Backstowing The filling of an underground void from which mineral has been extracted by replacement with spoil or other material.

Capital Items Items such as plant and machinery which are purchased for use over a number of years.

Capping (or overtipping) Process of covering consolidated lagoon deposits, generally with a layer of coarse discard.

CARBS Computer program for visual assessment used by NCB's ORE on major projects (usually new mines).

Coal Preparation Plant Process plant applying physical and mechanical processes to run-of-mine to make it suitable for particular uses.

Coarse Discard Waste material from the coal washing process with a particle size greater than 0.5mm.

COBA Cost benefit analysis computer program for evaluating economic benefits of highway schemes.

Colliery A deep coal mining operation which incorporates the mine, coal preparation plant, engineering and materials supply installations along with facilities for mining operatives.

Compaction The process by which the density of material is increased by rolling or by the passage of other mechanical plant to achieve closer packing of soil particles by expulsion of air.

Consolidation The time-dependent process by which soil particles are packed more closely together under the influence of loading through the expulsion of water.

Deep Mining Mining in which access to the mineral deposits is obtained by means of shafts or drifts as opposed to excavation from the surface.

Depreciation A proportion of the original cost of a capital item which is charged to the profit and loss account each year.

Dirt	General term for any extraneous material associated with the coal.
Discounted Cashflow	A technique for allowing different investment alternatives to be evaluated and compared. For a full discussion of discounted cashflow, see "Investment Appraisal in the Public Sector" H.M. Treasury, 1982.
Discount Rate	The rate used in a discounted cashflow calculation.
Drivage	The activity of cutting an underground roadway for access to coal face, transportation of run-of-mine and supplies, and for ventilation purposes.
Effluent	Waste water from a trade or process, or water from a surface or underground drainage operation which may be discharged to sewer or watercourse.
Equivalent Annual Cost	A technique which allows different cashflow profiles to be compared. It does so by reducing each to the Equivalent Annual Cost which would produce the same Net Present Value as the relevant cashflow.
Filter Cake	The partially dewatered product from the filtration process.
Filter Press	A batch process of pressure filter. Used for dewatering slurries containing fine solids (less than 0.5mm).
Filtration	A process for separating solids from liquids by allowing the liquid to pass through a finely woven cloth which retains the solids using vacuum or pressure to accelerate the separation.
Fines Discard	Waste material from the coal cleaning process with particle size less than 0.5mm.
Froth Flotation	A process for cleaning fine coal in which coal particles with the aid of reagents become attached to air bubbles in a liquid medium and float as a froth thus being separated from fine clays, etc., (known as tailings).
Gateside Pack	Tightly rammed material enclosed in walls of stone built on each side of a deep mine roadway to limit deterioration due to roof convergence following coal extraction.

Grading	The proportions of various grain sizes in a particulate material (well graded implies more or less uniform distribution from coarse to fine, poorly graded implies uniformity in size or lack of continuous distribution).
Greenfield Site	An area usually in agricultural or open use, which is proposed to be developed for mining or other industrial purposes.
Interest	Payments for the use of Loan Capital.
Lagoons	Settlement areas for material wholly or mainly in solution or suspension. Containments on tipping sites are generally constructed of coarse discard into which slurry or tailings in suspension are pumped to allow sedimentation of the solids and the discharge or re-use of the clarified supernatant water.
Leachate	Liquid that has percolated through soil or other medium and become polluted.
Life	The period of time over which a particular option is assessed.
Mineral Planning Authority	Local Authority responsible for the control of mineral workings under the Minerals Planning Act (usually the County Council).
Minestone	Unburnt colliery spoil, used for constructional purposes.
Moisture Content	Percentage by weight of total material.
MOSS	Computer program used in highway assessment studies.
Mulching	Laying of organic materials onto soil to improve its capacity to support vegetation by providing nutrients and improving soil structure, texture and moisture holding capacity.
Net Present Cost	The discounted value of a future stream of cash outflows. See also Net Present Value.
Net Present Value	The discounted value of a future stream of cashflows. For a fuller discussion, see "Investment Appraisal in the Public Sector", H.M. Treasury, 1982.

Opencast Mining	Mining of deposits in one or more seams by excavation from the surface after removal of the overlying deposits.
Operating Costs	Costs of materials and labour and other items used in the day to day operations.
Outturn Prices	Prices (and costs) expressed after taking account of assumed levels of inflation.
Overburden	Worthless rock or soil over the valuable mineral e.g. in an opencast mine.
Overheads	Costs which are not directly identifiable with any particular activity.
Poaching	Concentration of hoof marks and waterlogging on grazing land ususally at base of gradients
Raw Coal	Coal which has received no preparation other than possibly screening or crushing.
Real Prices	Prices (and costs) expressed in constant money terms without any allowance for inflation.
Reclamation	Combination of restoration and aftercare. In common usage the recovery of an area despoiled by industrial dereliction to beneficial use.
Restoration	After regarding of landform, sub-soiling, top-soiling and soil making process.
Ripping	Act of breaking to relieve compaction of soil forming materials (usually carried out by bulldozer - drawn heavy duty ripper or long angled steel tooth).
Run-of-mine	Raw mineral as raised from coal face prior to screening, crushing or preparation.
Run-off	Portion of rainfall that is not absorbed by deep strata, but is utilised by vegetation, lost by evaporation or finds it way into streams or surface flow.
Stripping	Process of removing soil forming materials in layers and respreading materials elsewhere (process usually carried out by motorised scrapers).
Screening	The separation of solid materials of different sizes by causing part to remain on a surface provided with apertures through which the remainder passes.

Seam	A stratum or layer or bed of coal or other mineral (generally applied to large deposits of coal).
Slurry	A suspension of fine raw coal with a particle size nominally less than 0.5mm in an aqueous medium.
Spoil	Waste (non coal) material extracted as a result of coal mining, variously known as dirt, waste, refuse, ash.
Spoil Heap	A tip of mining waste which is accumulated or deposited wholly or mainly in a solid state and not in solution or suspension.
Stacker Spreader	Device used in tipping of spoil which transfers and places spoil (also called radial spreader).
Stowage	Space from which mineral has been extracted and has been filled with waste.
Sub-soil	Weathered rock or soil lying immediately below top-soil (contains almost no organic matter).
Tailings	Reject from froth flotation process following the recovery of fine coal from slurries.
Thickening	The concentration of the solids in a suspension resulting in a product with a higher concentration of solids than in the original suspension. The process is often assisted by the use of flocculating agents.
Tining	Method by which top layers of restoration profiles are spiked to aerate soil, assist drainage and relieve compaction.
Tip	A spoil heap or lagoon.
Top-soil	Surface layer of soil rich in organic matter which provides physical support and nutrients to plants.
Visual Envelope Map (VEM)	Area or land within which a spoil tip can be seen.
Void	Space behind advancing coal face left by mining of coal. Local terms are goaf or waste.

EVALUATIVE FRAMEWORK

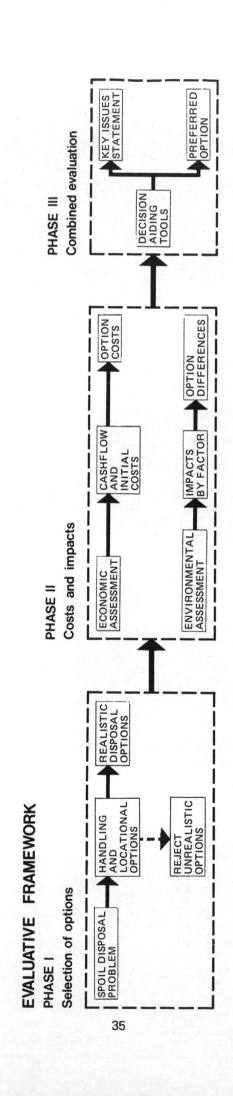

EVALUATIVE FRAMEWORK

PHASE I
Selection of options

SPOIL DISPOSAL PROBLEM

HANDLING AND LOCATIONAL OPTIONS

REJECT UNREALISTIC OPTIONS

REALISTIC DISPOSAL OPTIONS

PHASE II
Costs and impacts

ECONOMIC ASSESSMENT

CASHFLOW AND INITIAL COSTS

OPTION COSTS

ENVIRONMENTAL ASSESSMENT

IMPACTS BY FACTOR

OPTION DIFFERENCES

PHASE III
Combined evaluation

KEY ISSUES STATEMENT

DECISION AIDING TOOLS

PREFERRED OPTION

PHASE I – SELECTION OF OPTIONS

PHASE I – SELECTION OF OPTIONS

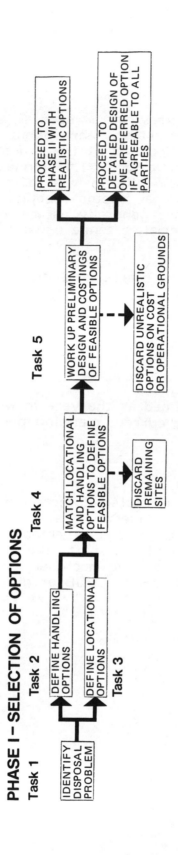

Task 1

IDENTIFY DISPOSAL PROBLEM

Task 2

DEFINE HANDLING OPTIONS

Task 3

DEFINE LOCATIONAL OPTIONS

Task 4

MATCH LOCATIONAL AND HANDLING OPTIONS TO DEFINE FEASIBLE OPTIONS

DISCARD REMAINING SITES

Task 5

WORK UP PRELIMINARY DESIGN AND COSTINGS OF FEASIBLE OPTIONS

DISCARD UNREALISTIC OPTIONS ON COST OR OPERATIONAL GROUNDS

PROCEED TO PHASE II WITH REALISTIC OPTIONS

PROCEED TO DETAILED DESIGN OF ONE PREFERRED OPTION IF AGREEABLE TO ALL PARTIES

qu.1.1   Tonnes or cubic metres can be used as appropriate, providing one measure is used consistently throughout. The Equivalent Annual Cost indicator can be calculated at the end of Phase II Economic in either unit. A conversion factor of 1.75 tonnes per cubic metre may be used for coarse spoil (being the average of compacted and bulked spoil) as necessary, if a local factor particular to that colliery is not available. Fines are generally estimated as the weight or volume of dry equivalent material, a tonne usually equating to a cubic metre.

qu.1.2, 1.3,1.4
         Distinguish between coarse and fines if handled and disposed of separately.

qu.1.4   This is usually defined as the year in which the design capacity (as incorporated in the current planning permission) is likely to be met.

qu.1.5   The difficulties of accurately forecasting spoil production are recognised but this question seeks to identify whether any major changes in spoil output are expected and if so when - such as the opening of a new drift or shaft, the closure of a colliery, the introduction of new coal cutting machinery or a change in marketing (e.g. higher ash content sold to CEGB or different blending with opencast).

qu.1.6   The question would be relevant for example where investment in dewatering equipment is planned which would change the composition of the fines to be disposed of.

TASK 1. IDENTIFY DISPOSAL PROBLEM

a]   <u>Existing Collieries</u>

1.1 What type/quantities of spoil are currently produced per annum?

        Coarse

        Fines (specify in what form)

1.2 Where is it disposed of?

        List sites

1.3 How is it transported there?

        List methods

1.4 In what year is tipping capacity reached at this (these) sites?

        Give years

1.5 From this year (as 1.4) onwards, are there any changes expected in annual spoil production from current levels due to:-

    i]   Higher/lower coal output
    ii]   Different mining methods
    iii] Different marketing?

    (If so – give increased or decreased quantities and year of occurrence)

1.6 Are there any changes that will affect the nature of spoil to be disposed?

    (If so – give details and dates)

qu.1.7   Note here if there are proposals to link any workings underground or combine Run of Mine from different collieries into a centralised Coal Preparation Plant.

qu.1.8   This question is very important as it defines the tipping capacity to be met by each of the options. This should be related to the expected remaining life of the colliery, based on estimated reserves. This is acknowledged to be politically sensitive and need not be revealed in answer to this question. Nevertheless, it could influence the outcome. The objective is to look sufficiently far into the future to allow sensible planning decisions to be taken and to give security of tipping space to the particular colliery operation. It is suggested that about a 20 year's tipping life be examined although, in some cases, for example shorter life collieries, a lesser period will be appropriate.

qu.1.9   See notes on question 1.1

qu.1.10   See notes on question 1.8

SELECTION OF OPTIONS - cont'd

1.7 Can the location of
spoil arisings be
altered, e.g. linking
workings underground?

    (If so – give
       details)

1.8 What tipping capacity
is required to be met
by the disposal options
to be considered?

       Coarse

       Fines

b] New Mines

1.9 What type/quantities of
spoil will be produced
per annum?

       Coarse

       Fines (specify
       in what form)

1.10 What tipping capacity
is required?

Output Task 1 –

Define Annual Disposal Capacity
Required for Expected Spoil
Production :

---

qu.2.1   This would include conveyor, dump trucks, tankers, pipeline, rail wagons, canal barges, etc.

qu.2.2   Surface mobile plant are easily transferable but fixed plant may be more difficult.

qu.2.3   This would include rail access (either with sidings available or capable of establishment), or canal or harbour access.

qu.2.4   Answers should only be given for those means of transport which present realistic options, bearing in mind the response to the previous question. Give numbers of lorry/train/barge movements depending on capacity, or diameter of pipeline.

SELECTION OF OPTIONS -   cont'd

TASK 2. DEFINE HANDLING OPTIONS

a]   Existing Collieries

2.1   What methods of handling
      spoil are currently used
      at the colliery?

              (List methods)

2.2   Could these existing
      methods be extended or
      re-used at another site?

              Yes
              No

a] & b]   Existing Collieries
           and New Mines

2.3   What means of access are
      available at the colliery
      site (in addition to
      those at 2.1) e.g. water,
      rail?

              (List means)

2.4   What scale of transport
      would be required to
      carry the daily volume
      of spoil?

Output Task 2 -

Define Preliminary Handling
Options :

a]   Local (On-site or adjacent) disposal sites comprise land within or
          immediately adjoining the colliery where access to disposal options
          does not need to use the public network.

qu.3.1   Detailed maps of the locality, generally at the scale of 1:10,000 will
          be required for this search, together with knowledge of local circum-
          stances and consideration of geology and stability factors. Approx-
          imate capacities should be estimated in relation to surface areas,
          topography and average depth of possible tipping, making simple
          volumetric calculations from sections.
          If a site will not be available until some time in the future, give
          expected date of availability.

qu.3.2   Even if the NCB cannot currently see a way to acquiring the land, this
          should not rule out an option at this stage in that other arrangements
          may be possible in consultation with the MPA. A final check on the
          feasibility of an option is made in question 4.3.

qu.3.4   This question is designed to elicit any physical constraints that may
          prevent the site accommodating lagoons. The acceptability or not of
          lagoons to the Mineral Planning Authority would also be considered
          within the design of disposal options.

SELECTION OF OPTIONS - cont'd

TASK 3. DEFINE LOCATIONAL OPTIONS

3a] Local (On-site or Adjacent)

3.1 Are there any suitable
sites (excluding
those where previous
applications have
failed, unless circum-
stances have changed)?

    Yes

(If Yes - List sites
and give capacities)

    No

(If No - go straight
to 3b)

3.2 Does NCB own this/these
sites?

    Yes

    No

(If No - can NCB obtain
it/them by:
i] Purchase
ii] Land Swaps?)

3.3 Is the capacity of this/
these sites sufficient
to meet tipping require-
ments?

    Yes

    No

(If No - go to 3b for
excess)

3.4 Can fines in suspension
be accommodated under
this option either by
lagooning or other means?

    Yes
(If Yes - state which)

    No

(If No - reconsider
coal prep.)

qu.3.5   This question identifies any options where a GDO tip might be brought under planning control as part of an overall package for a new tip. This is more likely to take place if the new site is adjacent to a GDO tip although it is a matter of negotiation between the NCB and MPA as to whether it is brought into the planning application procedure.

qu.3.6   Water Authorities are likely to raise objections to tipping within 1km of public boreholes and to seek special controls in the vicinity of aquifers and flood plains. They will also be responsible for controlling pipeline discharge into coastal waters.

qu.3.10   MAFF will provide advice, without prejudice to its formal response to any eventual planning application, on the grade of land from the published 1" to 1 mile agricultural classification maps, supplemented where possible by local knowledge and/or more detailed survey work if already available. (No definitive statement on the grade of land can be made without a detailed site survey.)

SELECTION OF OPTIONS - cont'd

3.5 Are there any GDO tips that would be brought into a scheme?

       Yes

       No

3.6 Is there likely to be an objection from the Water Authority to tipping on the site(s)?

       Yes

       No

3.7 Would spoil tipping sterilise other minerals?

       Yes

       No

3.8 What are the existing uses on the site(s)?

3.9 If the land is not agricultural would spoil tipping enable restoration or improved drainage?

       Yes

       No

3.10 If the land is agricultural what grade is it?

       Give grade

qu.3.11   MAFF can be expected to object to disposal schemes on Grades I and II land or where land of a lower acgricultural quality is available. MAFF have the power to sustain their objection through to Ministerial level. MAFF also have licensing powers over dumping at sea to safeguard fisheries interests.

Task 3a   The output of this task and 3b, 3c should be the definition of preliminary options. Options should be able to match the capacity required at qu.1.8. Individual options may comprise one site or a combination of sites. Sites can be combined from any of the three locational categories, on-site, local off-site and remote. Where different sites are combined, an assumed order of working needs to be defined. Reasons should be given for combining sites in a particular way and for dismissing sites.

b]   Local (Off-site) disposal sites are close to but not immediately adjacent to the colliery and where access is by means of the public transport network

qu.3.12   See notes on question 3.1. MAFF may be able to help in the identification of such options.

SELECTION OF OPTIONS - cont'd

3.11 What are MAFF's views on
the use of the site(s)?

Output Task 3a -

Define Preliminary On-site or
Adjacent Options (with reasons) :

3b] Local (Off-site)

Land Based

3.12 Are there any sites with
opportunities for environmental gain (give capac-
ities)? e.g.

    i]   Other mineral workings
        (sand & gravel/rock
        quarries requiring
        restoration)

        Yes

        (List sites and state
        whether the mineral
        operator is prepared
        to tender for the
        transport and disposal
        of spoil there)

        No

    ii]   Other sites (including
        low lying, poorly drained
        ground)

        Yes

        (List sites)

        No

qu.3.14   Checks may need to be made with NCB's Minestone Executive.

qu.3.17   See notes on questions 3.6 and 3.11

SELECTION OF OPTIONS - cont'd

3.13 Are there any sites with opportunities for combined tipping
(give capacities)? e.g.

   i]   Opencast sites existing
        or programmed

             Yes

             (List sites and state
              whether OE prepared to
              create a space for deep
              mined spoil)

             No

   ii] Household refuse sites
        operated or proposed by
        the Waste Disposal Authority

             Yes

             (List sites and state
              whether WDA have oppor-
              tunities for co-disposal
              or use of spoil as blinding
              material)

             No

3.14 Has the suitability of the spoil
for such reclamation work been
checked?

3.15 Are there any other sites
available?

3.16 Can the NCB acquire the land
or use of the land in above
sites?

             Yes

             No

3.17 Are there likely to be
any objections from the
Water Authority or MAFF?

             Yes

             No

53

Task 3b   See notes for output task 3a

SELECTION OF OPTIONS -   cont'd

Sea Based

3.18 Are there any suitable
    dumping grounds?

3.19 What capacity can be
    accommodated there?

3.20 Are there likely to be
    objections from MAFF,
    Crown Estate Commiss
    ioners or Water
    Authorities?

3.21 Are licences likely to
    be forthcoming for
    continued/increased
    dumping in these areas?

Output Task 3b -

Define Preliminary Local
Off-site Options (with
reasons) :

c)   Remote disposal sites are taken to be greater than about 15kms from
         the colliery.

qu.3.22   See notes on questions 3.1 and 3.12/3.13.

qu.3.23   See notes on question 3.14.

qu.3.26   See notes on questions 3.6 and 3.11

SELECTION OF OPTIONS - cont'd

3c] <u>Remote</u>

3.22 Are there any sites or voids with opportunities for large scale reclamation within a feasible range along any main transport corridors?

      Yes

    (List sites and give capacities)

      No

3.23 Has the suitability of the spoil for such reclamation work been checked?

3.24 Are any of these sites owned by NCB?

      Yes

      No

    If No -

     i] Can NCB acquire them?

    ii] Is the mineral operator prepared to tender for the transport and disposal of spoil there?

3.25 Is the capacity sufficiently large to justify the installation of special handling infrastructure?

      Yes

      No

    If No - dismiss option

3.26 Are there likely to be any objections from the Water Authority or MAFF?

      Yes

      No

Task 3c   See notes for output Task 3a

SELECTION OF OPTIONS - cont'd

3.27 Can the discard output
of any collieries be
combined to produce a
more viable scheme?

        Yes

If so - which?

        No

Output Task 3c -

Define Preliminary Remote
Options (with reasons) :

Output Tasks 3a, 3b and 3c -

Define Combined
On-site/Off-site/Remote
Options (with reasons) :

Task 4

These questions provide a check on the preliminary options to ensure that they are feasible in terms of handling and transport arrangements (of particular relevance to the off-site options) and acquisition arrangements.

qu.4.1   The distance threshold of transport modes relates either to physical factors, (e.g. the maximum throughput or length of different types of conveyance) or to economic factors, (e.g. the distances over which return train loads can be transported within a staff shift).

qu.4.2   The emphasis of this question is on the word "undue" so that only realistic options should be taken forward into Phase II.

qus. 4.2 and 4.3

Whether or not to dismiss options at this stage is a matter to be agreed between the NCB and MPA. A common sense approach should be taken.

TASK 4. MATCH PRELIMINARY LOCATIONAL AND HANDLING OPTIONS

4.1 Are feasible off-site
   locational options within
   the distance threshold of
   available transport modes?

   Yes

   If No - dismiss option

4.2 Will the intended transport modes and routes for
   off-site options cause
   undue environmental disturbance (e.g. excessive
   number of lorries through
   villages over a number of
   years)?

   If Yes - dismiss option

   No

4.3 Can NCB acquire the land
   or working agreements at
   the short-listed sites?

   Yes

   If No - dismiss option

Output Task 4

Define Feasible Options :

---

qu.5.2 Sketch plans should be produced for each option to be studied further, usually at a scale of 1:10,000 or larger as appropriate, to indicate the assumed scheme of working in sufficient detail to indicate areas to be soil stripped, tipped or restored each year (or span of years). This level of detail is a necessary basis from which to apply unit rates for each activity to generate the costings information in Phase II Economic. The sketch plans should also indicate assumed impact amelioration measures, e.g. earth mounding and screening, as a basis for the assessment of site specific environmental aspects in Phase II Environmental. This exercise will also test the feasibility of the schemes and if any are shown to be unrealistic they can be discarded before moving onto Phase II.

SELECTION OF OPTIONS -   cont'd

TASK 5. WORK UP PRELIMINARY DESIGN AND COSTINGS FOR EACH FEASIBLE OPTION

5.1   Discard any totally
      unrealistic options on
      cost grounds if agree-
      able to all parties

5.2   Produce a sketch plan
      for each option with
      an approximate phasing
      timetable

Output Task 5 :   Proceed to Phase II of Framework with
                                   Realistic Options

                                   Unless one preferred option is agreeable to
                                   all parties.

PHASE II - ECONOMIC ASSESSMENT

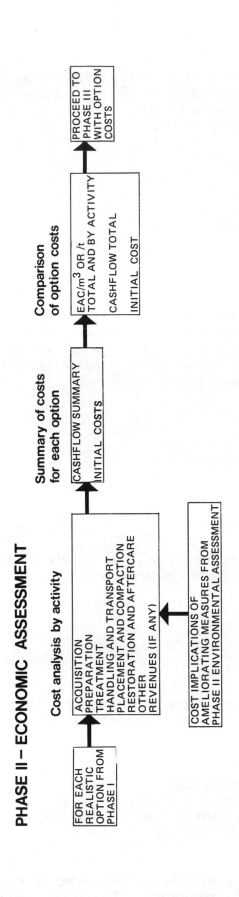

PHASE II – ECONOMIC ASSESSMENT

Cost analysis by activity

FOR EACH REALISTIC OPTION FROM PHASE I

ACQUISITION
PREPARATION
TREATMENT
HANDLING AND TRANSPORT
PLACEMENT AND COMPACTION
RESTORATION AND AFTERCARE
OTHER
REVENUES (IF ANY)

COST IMPLICATIONS OF AMELIORATING MEASURES FROM PHASE II ENVIRONMENTAL ASSESSMENT

Summary of costs for each option

CASHFLOW SUMMARY
INITIAL COSTS

Comparison of option costs

EAC/m³ OR /t TOTAL AND BY ACTIVITY
CASHFLOW TOTAL
INITIAL COST

PROCEED TO PHASE III WITH OPTION COSTS

For some disposal options under consideration some of the answers to questions in this Cost Analysis section may contain commercially sensitive information. In this situation the amount of detail that can be disclosed will be a matter for discretion by the particular NCB Area.

qu.1.1, 1.2

Ensure that all the parcels of land for a particular option are covered. Both answers go forward into the cash flow summary as a scheme cost. The purchase price for land that the NCB does not already own is likely to be greater than the selling price of land it does own because of hope value.

qu.1.3 a & b

These forms of tenure will be rarely used because of the length of time disposal schemes occupy land.

qu.1.3 c   This includes the costs of royalties to Crown Estate Commissioners for beach tipping and MAFF licence fees for sea dumping.

qu.1.4   Wayleave payments may be necessary where a conveyor or pipeline is laid across someone else's land or where discharge facilities are provided on non-NCB land after a rail or canal haul. Wayleaves are generally payable annually.

qu.1.5   Other costs may include compensation to existing farmers to leave land already in NCB ownership. The amount will vary depending on whether the farmer has a tenancy or a licence. The purchase of any property due to be demolished or left vacant would also be included here.

PHASE II – ECONOMIC ASSESSMENT

Cost Analysis by Activity

		Initial/ Recurring	Cost £	Comments
1.0	**Acquisition**			
1.1	If the site(s) is already owned by NCB, what is its value (i.e. likely selling price)?	I		
1.2	If the site(s) is not owned but can be purchased by NCB, what is the likely purchase price? (area ha x price per ha plus legal fees, etc.)	I		
1.3	If the site(s) cannot be purchased what is:-			
	a] the likely annual rental cost?	R		
	b] the cost of obtaining working rights?	I/R		
	c] the cost of obtaining royalties or licences?	I/R		
1.4	What is the cost, if any, of obtaining wayleaves or other access costs for transport means?	I/R		
1.5	Are there any other costs associated with site acquisition or usage? If so, itemise and give costs	I/R		

69

2.0 Site Preparation

This should include costs associated with the use of scapers, excavators and dump trucks, for preparation as opposed to operation. If the same vehicles are used for both, then initial costs must only be included once, but care must be taken to ensure that recurring costs for preparation and operation are included in the relevant sections.

qu.2.1   Include all demolition costs, net of any revenues which may arise from the disposal of demolished items.

qu.2.2   Include all costs associated with moving items such as power lines. Any separate land acquisition or wayleave costs associated with this heading should be included here if not already listed in Section 1.

qu.2.3   Where progressive restoration is being undertaken, soil stripping costs and some restoration costs will be combined. It is acceptable to include such costs here with a note in Section 6 (Restoration), but they must not be double counted. The cost of grassing soil heaps and weed control should also be included.

qu.2.4   Accommodation costs may include fencing, diversion of footpaths and off-tip landscaping. The latter includes perimeter planting both on NCB land and elsewhere where required.

qu.2.5   Include costs of filter drainage systems and toe drains for the proposed tip and any necessary culverting of streams.

qu.2.6   Include any replacement/refurbishment costs if these are likely to arise over the life of the tip. Include any costs arising after the site preparation period is complete (eg extra fencing).

qu.2.7   Do not include sunk costs unless there is a transfer value (see question 8.5). Where there is a fixed conveyor include base for conveyors here (where necessary, on uncompacted land) and include conveyors in Section 4 (Handling & Transport)

qu.2.8   Include refurbishment costs.

ECONOMIC ASSESSMENT -   cont'd

2.0   Site(s) Preparation

		Initial/ Recurring	Cost £	Comments
2.1	What are total demolition and surface debris clearance costs?	I		
2.2	What are the costs of diverting public utilities?	I		
2.3	What are the costs of soil stripping and storage (area x depth x unit rate)?	R		
2.4	What are the accommodation costs (fencing, land- scaping, etc.)?	I		
2.5	What are the costs of drainage (includ- ing any culverting)?	I		
2.6	What are the annual costs of maintaining fencing and drainage systems?	R		
2.7	What are the civil works costs (haul routes, access routes, bridges, etc.)?	I		
2.8	What are the annual costs of maintaining these civil works?	R		

qu.2.9   Include all other preparation costs not already listed.   These could
          include hardstanding, weighbridges, provision of transportation access
          facilities not already shown under 2.7 and erection of screens, etc.

ECONOMIC ASSESSMENT –   cont'd

	Initial/ Recurring	Cost £	Comments
2.9 Identify any other costs of site(s) preparation	I		
2.10 If option relates only to coarse discard or if fines treatment costs are common to each option go to Section 4			

3.0 Fines Treatment
This section is important where options use different methods.

qu.3.2   A current quotation/estimate is required.

qu.3.3   Include only cash costs, ie exclude depreciation (the analysis will take this into account via the initial cost).

qu.3.4   If appropriate, include these costs under Section 5.

qu.3.5   Include costs of inlet/outlet structures, associated pumps and treatment equipment for supernatant water if a new operation. Include construction costs where these are separately identifiable e.g. for a freestanding lagoon. Where retaining walls are formed from coarse discard within an existing tip costs may already be accounted for in Section 5. Pipeline costs are to be included at qu.4.5. Overtipping costs are to be included in qu.6.12.

qu.3.6   Include costs of maintaining lagoon monitoring installations.

qu.3.7   Include pumping stations.

ECONOMIC ASSESSMENT -   cont'd

		Initial/ Recurring	Cost £	Comments
3.0	Treatment of Fines			
a]	For options using dewatering process			
3.1	Note type of equipment.........			
3.2	What is the initial cost of this equip- ment?	I		
3.3	What are the annual operating costs of this equipment (labour, maintenance, power, etc.)?	R		
3.4	What is the cost of constructing emergency lagoon capacity?	I		
b]	For options using lagoons			
3.5	What is the cost of constructing lagoons, (labour, bulldozers, fuel, etc.)?	I		
3.6	What are the annual operating costs (power, etc.)?	R		
c]	For options using discharge pipelines			
3.7	What is the cost of constructing or extending a pipeline?	I		
3.8	What are the annual operating costs (power, etc.)?	R		

4.0 Handling & Transport
Answer this section separately for coarse and fines discard if handled differently.

qu.4.2   If re-using existing plant enter only the cost of relocation. If the purchase of new equipment here allows the reuse of existing equipment elswhere enter the sale proceeds under question 8.5. Capital costs of conveyors are usually based on a per metre rate.

qu.4.3   Annual operating costs of conveyors relate to maintenance (usually per metre rate) and power (horsepower rated). Replacement belting and structure is usually included in the maintenance cost. The maintenance costs of a stacker spreader are often estimated as a proportion of the capital costs of the mechanical equipment.

qu.4.5   Include number and capacities of vehicles (dump trucks, etc.)

qu.4.6   Note life associated with surface mobile plant. If some vehicles are used for other duties besides spoil disposal include only the relevant proportion.

qu.4.7   Ensure that non-cash costs, such as depreciation, are excluded from NCB internal plant pool rates.

ECONOMIC ASSESSMENT – cont'd

	Initial/ Recurring	Cost £	Comments

4.0 Handling and Transport

a] For options using conveyors

4.1 Note length of conveyor or stacker spreader

4.2 What is the initial cost of providing this fixed plant?	I		
4.3 What are the annual operating costs of this fixed plant (maintenance, power, etc.)?	R		
4.4 Note any other costs	I/R		

b] For options using off-highway transport

4.5 Identify equipment......

4.6 If NCB owned, what is the initial cost of providing these vehicles?	I		
4.7 What are the annual operating costs of these vehicles (drivers, maintenance, fuel, etc.)?	R		
4.8 If using contractors, what are the annual hire rates (annual movements x hire rate)?	R		
4.9 Note any other costs	I/R		

qu.4.14   Include numbers and capacities of vehicles (dump trucks, tankers, etc.)

qu.4.16   Exclude depreciation costs and any other non cash items.

qu.4.18   Such costs might be initial costs to cover road widening along the proposed route or access improvements at the colliery or disposal site, or operating costs to cover an on-going contribution to increased road maintenance charges along the route.

ECONOMIC ASSESSMENT – cont'd

		Initial/ Recurring	Cost £	Comments
c]	**For options using pipelines**			
4.10	Note length and type of pipeline			
4.11	What is the initial cost of providing this pipeline?	I		
4.12	What are the annual operating costs of this pipe-line (maintenance, power, etc.)?	R		
4.13	Note any other costs	I/R		
d]	**For options using road transport**			
4.14	Identify equipment.......			
4.15	If NCB owned, what is the initial cost of providing these vehicles?	I		
4.16	What are the annual operating costs of these vehicles (drivers, maintenance, fuel, etc.)?	R		
4.17	If using contractors what are the annual hire rates (annual movements x hire rates)?	R		
4.18	What costs would be payable to the High-way Authority?	I/R		
4.19	Note any other costs	I/R		

qu.4.20　　Under loading facilities include hoppers or loading shovel; concrete pad; any new track and/or signalling at origin end. Under unloading facilities include storage, conveyors or loading shovels, concrete pad and new track and/or signalling at destination end.

qu.4.22　　Include the costs of operating hoppers, conveyors and loading shovels, maintenance of facilities and track, and a contingency fund to cover any BR cancellation charges.

qu.4.23　　Costs of rail wagons vary with size and method of discharge. Where they are hired from BR the costs will be included in qu.4.25.

qu.4.24　　Ensure no double counting with qu.4.25 below.

ECONOMIC ASSESSMENT –	cont'd Initial/ Recurring	Cost £	Comments
e] For options using rail transport			
4.20 What are the initial costs of providing:-			
i] Loading facilities	I		
ii] Unloading facilities (elevators, hoppers, temporary storage,etc.)?	I		
(NB – if there is already a railhead at the colliery for coal, include only the cost of modifications for spoil use)			
4.21 What is the cost of providing emergency storage facilities?	I		
4.22 What are the annual operating costs of loading and unloading (labour, maintenance, power, etc.)?	R		
4.23 What is the cost of buying rail wagons (no. of rail wagons x unit rate)?	I		
4.24 What are the annual operating costs of rail wagons?	R		

qu.4.25   Annual freight charges have to be obtained from BR. To put forward a quotation the best combination of wagons per train, trains per shift and shifts per day have to be estimated.

qu.4.27   Under loading and unloading facilities include hoppers or loading shovel; concrete pad; any new road, conveyor or other access required to the canal side from the colliery not already listed in section 2 and any new loading or unloading equipment.

qu.4.28   Include only cash costs.

qu.4.29   Only if barge purchase is required.

ECONOMIC ASSESSMENT –	cont'd Initial/ Recurring	Cost £	Comments
4.25 What are the annual freight charges (no. of trains x BR freight rates)?	R		
4.26 Note any other costs	I/R		
f] For options using barging			
4.27 What are the initial costs of providing			
i] Loading facilities	I		
ii] Unloading facilities (elevators, hoppers, temporary storage, etc.)?	I		
4.28 What are the annual operating costs of loading and unloading (labour, maintenance, power, etc.)?	R		
4.29 What is the cost of buying barges (no. of barges x unit rate)?	I		
4.30 What are the annual freight charges (no. of barges x freight rates)?	R		
4.31 Note any other costs	I/R		

5.0 Placement & Compaction

qu.5.1   Include numbers and capacities of vehicles (loading shovels, bulldozers, refuelling bowsers, rollers, etc.)

qu.5.2 & 5.3
         See comments for qu.4.6 - 4.7

ECONOMIC ASSESSMENT – cont'd

	Initial/ Recurring	Cost £	Comments
5.0 Placement and Compaction			
5.1 Identify equipment			
5.2 If NCB owned, what is the cost of buying vehicles?	I		
5.3 What are the annual operating costs of these vehicles (drivers, maintenance, fuel, etc.)?	R		
5.4 If using contractors, what are the annual hire rates?	R		
5.5 Note any other costs	I/R		

6.0 Restoration and Aftercare

qu.6.1   Grading/levelling costs will normally have been covered by the inclusion of a bulldozer under qu.5.2. Include here costs of final treatment of spoil surface before soil replacement.

qu.6.3   These costs may have already been included under qu.2.3 where progressive restoration is being undertaken.

qu.6.4   Unit rates for drainage, fencing can vary dramatically with topography, type of soil and planning requirements. Planting and maintaining hedges may substitute for fencing. Include also costs of installing any water supplies and providing agricultural access roads.

qu.6.5   Cultivation includes ploughing, fertilizing, liming and harrowing. Planting costs will vary between grass seeding and tree planting and should be separately identified where applicable. Any secondary drainage treatment that may be required subsequently should also be included.

qu.6.6   These costs (fertilisers, etc.) will be incurred over a number of years after the land is returned to agriculture. If an average rate per area of land is being used, only the relevant proportion of this should be included in a given year.

qu.6.7   As with qu.6.1, only include such costs not already listed in Section 5.

qu.6.8   Do not double count with qu.2.4 and 2.6.

qu.6.9   Do not double count with Section 2 generally.

ECONOMIC ASSESSMENT - cont'd

	Initial/ Recurring	Cost £	Comments

6.0 Restoration and Aftercare

6.1 What are the costs of grading, ripping and liming of the spoil?	R		
6.2 What are the costs of overtipping lagoons?	I		
6.3 What are the costs of replacing and ripping sub- and top-soil and purchasing additional soil where required?	R		
6.4 What are the costs of drainage, fencing, etc.?	I		
6.5 What are the costs of cultivation and planting (area x unit rate)?	R		
6.6 What are the annual operating costs of aftercare (soil analysis, application of fertiliser, replacement of dead plants/trees, etc.)?	R		

Reclamation to Non-Agricultural Uses

6.7 What are the costs of grading and levelling?	I		
6.8 What are the costs of drainage, fencing, etc.?	I		
6.9 Note any other costs (e.g. provision of infrastructure)	I		

7.0 Other Costs

qu.7.1   Such costs might include design costs, contingency funds, special monitoring measures (particularly in the marine environment).

ECONOMIC ASSESSMENT – cont'd

	Initial/ Recurring	Cost £	Comments
7.0 Other Costs			
7.1 Itemise any other costs associated with disposal and not already listed above	I/R		

8.0 Revenues

qu.8.1   Estimate rental income for the years until each land parcel is brought into use within the scheme, if land was vested in the NCB or bought in advance.

qu.8.2   Only include a value here if NCB intends to sell the land.
The value would be expected to be about half the agricultural value in early years of return to agriculture.

qu.8.3   Rent will be obtainable from those parts returned to agriculture (exclude amenity woodland, etc.). Rental income may be less during aftercare period.

qu.8.5   An entry would be made here if, for example, an option involved the purchase of a new conveyor (entered under question 4.2) and this allowed the disposal of an existing conveyor in another part of NCB operations.

qu.8.6   Include a residual value where mobile plant is still within its write-off period at the end of tipping and could be transferred to another scheme. Scrap value usually only just covers the costs of dismantling fixed plant, so only include a value if relevant.

ECONOMIC ASSESSMENT -

		cont'd Initial/ Recurring	Cost £	Comments
8.0	**Revenues**			
8.1	What level of income could be expected on land already owned but not needed until later in the scheme?	R		
8.2	What is the likely value of the land when it is fully restored?	I		
8.3	What level of income could be expected from the land when it is fully restored?	R		
8.4	What income can be obtained from the sale of spoil?	R		
8.5	If this option allows NCB to dispose of land or plant, give sale proceeds.	I		
8.6	What is the terminal value, if any, associated with mobile plant?	I		

PHASE II – ECONOMIC

CASHFLOW SUMMARY

OPTION:

Discount Rate   5%
Number of Years Tipping
Average Spoil Tipped p.a. (cu.m. or tonnes)
Years to Start of Tipping

	TOTAL	£'000 at 198 /	198 /	198 /	etc. for 20 years
Disposal Quantities (cu.m or tonnes p.a.)					
1.0 Acquisition					
2.0 Site Preparation					
3.0 Treatment of Fines					
4.0 Handling & Transport					
5.0 Placement & Compaction					
6.0 Restoration and Aftercare					
7.0 Other Costs					
8.0 Revenues					
TOTAL CASHFLOW					
DISCOUNTED CASHFLOW					

E.A.C. per cubic metre or tonne

PHASE II – ECONOMIC

INITIAL COST SUMMARY

OPTION :

£'000 at 198   prices

ITEM	TOTAL COST	INITIAL COST IN YEAR					REMAINING INITIAL COSTS
		1 198 /	2 198 /	3	4	5	
Acquisition							
Preparation							
Treatment							
Handling & Transport							
Placement & Compaction							
Restoration & Aftercare							
Other							
Initial Revenues							

1st Year of Tipping 198 /8

TOTAL INITIAL COST £

93

PHASE II – ECONOMIC

SUMMARY OF OPTION COSTS

	Option A £	Option B £
Equivalent Annual Cost Per Cubic Metre or tonne of Spoil		
EACs by activity		
– Acquisition		
– Preparation		
– Treatment		
– Handling & Transport		
– Placement & Compaction		
– Restoration & Aftercare		
– Other		
– Revenues		
Cashflow Total		
Initial Cost		

PHASE II – ENVIRONMENTAL ASSESSMENT

PHASE II – ENVIRONMENTAL ANALYSIS

```
┌──────────────────┐      ┌──────────────────────────┐      ┌──────────────────┐      ┌──────────────────┐      ┌──────────────────┐
│ FOR EACH REALISTIC│─────▶│ ASSESSMENT OF EXISTING   │─────▶│ SUMMARIES OF     │─────▶│ OPTION           │─────▶│ PROCEED TO       │
│ OPTION FROM PHASE I│     │ QUALITY AND  IMPACTS     │      │ ENVIRONMENTAL    │      │ DIFFERENCES      │      │ PHASE III        │
└──────────────────┘      │                          │      │ IMPACTS          │      └──────────────────┘      │ WITH OPTION      │
                          │ VISUAL                   │      └──────────────────┘                                │ IMPACTS          │
                          │ LAND-USE                 │                                                          └──────────────────┘
                          │ ECOLOGY/HERITAGE/        │
                          │ RECREATION               │
                          │ WATER/AIR/NOISE          │
                          │ TRANSPORT                │
                          │ OTHER                    │
                          └──────────────────────────┘
                                      │
                                      ▼
                          ┌──────────────────────────┐
                          │ FEEDBACK ANY COST IMPLICATIONS│
                          │ OF AMELIORATING MEASURES TO   │
                          │ PHASE II ECONOMIC ANALYSIS    │
                          └──────────────────────────┘
```

Answers to the impact questions should include an assessment of the effect on different parties (for example residents and occupiers of properties; landowners; recreational visitors to the site or surroundings; travellers using nearby roads, footpaths or other routes; the local community and industries other than coal mining), together with timing and duration of the impact.

1.0 Visual

qu.1.1 This should record the significant landscape and built-form features, describing the nature and visual quality of land uses, the topographical character and vegetation.

qu.1.2 This information can normally be obtained from local planning authorities and documents such as Structure Plan and Local Plan reports. Include statutory designations and also any features of local importance.

qu.1.3 This information can normally be obtained from the Tree Preservation Officer of the local planning authority.

qu.1.4 Views from the main vantage points surrounding the site should be described, e.g. from roads, houses. Site record photographs are useful here.

Assessment of Existing Quality and Impacts

Initial Task

Define the study area by drawing
the approximate boundaries of
the area within which the proposed scheme would be visible or
have an effect.

1.0   Visual

A.   Existing Landscape/Visual Quality

1.1   Comment generally on
the existing landscape
quality and appearance
of:

a]   the site
b]   the surroundings
within the study
area

1.2   List any special land-
scape features or desig-
nations (e.g. Areas of
Outstanding Natural Beauty,
National Parks, Heritage
Coasts):

a]   on the site
b]   in the surroundings

1.3   Note any individual trees,
groups of trees or wood-
lands and whether covered
by Tree Preservation Orders:

a]   on the site
b]   adjacent to the site

1.4   Identify the main views
into the site noting any
features which screen
views

qu.1.5   Note also the use of this property, e.g. residential, school.

qu.1.6   This question and 1.7 can be answered by defining a visual envelope
           map (VEM) on say 1:25,000 scale maps, by taking a series of sections
           radiating out from the highest point of each tipping proposal. The
           contours crossing these section lines are then marked and the extent
           of visibility of the tip can then be checked. These limits of views
           of the site can also be verified by site visits. It is especially
           important to note the areas within these limits from which views of
           the site are restricted by trees and/or intermediate high ground.
           Intervening development may also obstruct views, thus causing a
           "shadow" on the VEM. Highlight any planned developments that will be
           affected.
           In order to illustrate and present the points raised in this section a
           variety of graphical techniques may be used if felt necessary. These
           may include techniques such as photomontage, measured perspectives,
           acetate overlays, computer generated perspectives, etc. Include
           schools, hospitals, etc. as sensitive uses.

qu.1.7   Include for example country parks. For the more distant parts of the
           VEM, it is only the significant features which need to be recorded.

qu.1.8   Include for example NCB tenancies and dependency of the local comm-
           unity on the mining industry.

qu.1.9   This will give an indication of the extent of pervasiveness of spoil
           disposal activities in a particular locality. The surrounding area
           can be defined as being within say 2km of the proposed site.

qu.1.10   Include for example screening mounds or new planting of trees on or
           adjacent to the site. Special features which could be incorporated
           in works around a site can have significant effects on reducing the
           visual impact of a new tip, but is is important to assess, for
           example, the time taken before a new tree screen becomes effective.

ENVIRONMENTAL ASSESSMENT – cont'd

B. Impact of Disposal Scheme

1.5 What distance from the edge of the disposal site is the nearest property?

1.6 Estimate the number of properties and other sensitive uses (existing and planned) which have a view of the site and are located:

a] within ½km of edge of disposal site

b] between ½km and 1km from the edge of the disposal site

1.7 List residential areas and other features which have a view of the site and are located:

a] within 1km and 2km of the disposal site

b] beyond 2km

1.8 Note any particular ownership patterns in the surrounding communities

1.9 What proportion of open land in the surrounding area has already been used or is committed for spoil disposal?

1.10 What features will ameliorate the impacts of the scheme and at what stage of development will these features become effective?

1.11 Note the visual impact of any lagoons in the option and identify any locations from which the following will be visible:

a] water surface

b] retaining walls

qu.1.12   This could include views of woods, open fields, a ridge that might be obstructed by the build up of a tip.

qu.1.13   Visual intrusiveness during the tipping scheme is important and the effect of any progressive restoration or changes in tipping location during a phased scheme should be assessed.

ENVIRONMENTAL ASSESSMENT   –   cont'd

1.12 Identify any views
which will be blocked
out by the scheme

1.13 Assess the degree to
which the scheme will
be visually intrusive.
Note any significant
differences during
the operations of the
scheme, intrusiveness
of the final form
and its after-use

2.0 Land Use Impacts

qu.2.2   Where farmland is involved state also the type of crop and how well the land is maintained. Check that the total for each land use together with any under question 2.6 equals the total site area.

qu.2.3   MAFF will usually need to undertake additional fieldwork to refine their earlier assessment of grading.

qu.2.4 and
qu.2.5   Such information will normally be available to NCB Estates Dept. It may be inappropriate to contact farmers when considering preliminary options for fear of causing blight, but MAFF may be in a position to privide advice.

qu.2.6   This includes existing tipping land whether GDO tips or under planning control. For land currently having public access, note intensity of use. Check that the total for each land use together with any under question 2.2 equals the total site area.

qu.2.8   If known, specify the type of future agricultural use, e.g. for pasture or arable farming.

ENVIRONMENTAL ASSESSMENT - cont'd

2.0 **Land Use**

A. **Existing Land Use**

2.1 Identify any properties on site affected by the option

a] **For Existing Agricultural Land**

2.2 Quantify the land taken by the scheme by current use of land

2.3 What is MAFF's assessment of the land grade?

2.4 What proportion of the existing farm unit does the tipping site comprise?

2.5 Comment on the viability of the remaining farm unit

b] **For Existing Non-agricultural Land**

2.6 Quantify the land taken by the scheme by current use of land

c] **For Sea**

2.7 Are there any fisheries interests represented in the proposed dumping ground?

B. **Restoration and After-use**

2.8 How much land will be restored to agriculture and to what type of agricultural use?

qu.2.10   The need for lagoons within the tip may affect the speed at which progressive restoration can occur. Give details of this effect, if known.

qu.2.11   This involves restoration progressively following behind tipping operations without storage of soil (except from the first tranche). It does not necessarily mean restoration in annual phases.

qu.2.12   Check that the answer is consistent with the after-uses proposed under question 2.8.

qu.2.13   This situation would occur if tipping is into an old quarry, for example.

qu.2.14   MAFF will advise on the basis of local circumstances and standard of restoration envisaged. As a rule of thumb, MAFF considers that land will usually drop a grade or two sub-grades. The rate of improvement thereafter will depend on the skill of the farmer but will usually occur only very gradually.

qu.2.15   Where the site involves changes to a degraded site note any improvements which could be achieved during or after the tipping scheme.

qu.2.16   Where a proposed after-use is recreational or industrial, it may relieve pressure on agricultural land in other nearby locations. Comment on the quantity and quality of agricultural land affected in this way.

qu.2.17   Any employment generated by an industrial after-use would count as a benefit of that option.

2.9 What other after-uses
will result and what will
be their areas?

2.10 If lagoons are required
in this scheme, what
impact will there be for
the restoration programme?

a]   For Agricultural
Restoration

2.11 Will the restoration be
progressive?

2.12 How much of the site will
the available topsoil and
sub-soil be used to cover?

2.13 If insufficient restoration materials are
available on site (in
whole or in part), what
restoration treatment
will apply?

2.14 What is the expected
land grade when this
restoration occurs and
how will this improve
over succeeding years?

b]   For Other After-uses

2.15 Will these after-uses
ameliorate or improve
existing environmental
conditions of the site?

2.16 Will they relieve
development pressure
elsewhere?

2.17 Will they create
employment?

3.0 Ecological/Heritage/Recreational

qu.3.1   This information will be available from the Mineral Planning Auth-
         ority. Include sites of Special Scientific Interests (SSSIs, PSSSIs),
         nature reserves and areas of local interest, rare plants/insect
         species, marine life.

qu.3.2   Organisations such as Nature Conservancy Council, Royal Society for
         the Protection of Birds (RSPB), British Ecological Society, Fauna and
         Flora Preservation Society, will provide specialist advice if required
         but this is unlikely to be necessary at this stage. The Nature
         Conservancy Council would be consulted formally at the planning
         application stage for sites containing SSSIs.

qu.3.4   Include listed buildings, historic ruins, common land, church land,
         allotments. Such information will be available from the Mineral
         Planning Authority.

qu.3.5   The National Trust or the Ancient Monument Society would advise but
         this is unlikely to be necessary.

qu. 3.6   Local planning authorities will have the routes (footpaths, bridle-
and   ways, cycle ways, etc.) and spaces documented; additional information
qu. 3.7   on usage could be obtained from local groups of Ramblers Associations.
          In some cases small surveys of usage may need to be conducted.
          Comment on any changes in routes or footpaths which are used by the
          local community which may have a severance effect.

3.0 **Ecological/Heritage**
Recreational

3.1 List any significant
ecological habitats and
whether covered by stat-
utory designation:

    a]   on the site
    b]   in close proximity
        to the site

3.2 Will any of these be
lost or disturbed? State
whether on-site or
distance from edge of
site

3.3 Comment on the severity
of disturbance and the
extent of recreatability

3.4 List any man-made features
of importance or land
with special rights:

    a]   on the site
    b]   in close proximity
        to the site

3.5 Comment on the loss or
severity of disturbance
of any such heritage
features and whether
effects are temporary
(pending restoration)
or permanent. State
whether on-site or
distance from edge of
site

3.6 List any footpaths or
other recreational
features and comment
on their usage:

    a]   on the site
    b]   in the surroundings

3.7 Comment on the loss of
or disturbance to any
footpaths etc., and
whether effects are
temporary or permanent

4.0 Water/Air/Noise

qu.4.1   Contact the local Water Authority for any extra details on existing water supply sources or drainage characteristics of the site and its locality. Include details of water courses, flood plains, springs, aquifers. Note the permeability of underlying strata.

qu.4.2   If there is any water pollution prior to tipping, give details of its source(s) and any quantification possible.

qu.4.3   Give details, where appropriate, of any special precautions which may be necessary during and after tipping, e.g. to protect aquifers or other water supplies.

4.0 Water/Air/Noise

4.1 Identify any relevant hydrological features:

a] on the site
b] in the surroundings

4.2 Note any existing sources of water pollution and/or any sensitive features:

a] on the site
b] in the surroundings

4.3 What measures will be taken to control water pollution from surface run-off, leachates, etc?

4.4 Comment on any existing sources of air pollution and ambient levels of dust:

a] on the site
b] in the surroundings

4.5 Note any local climatic conditions (prevailing winds, etc.) that affect the exposure/shelter of the site

4.6 What measures will be taken to control any potential dust problems from tipping operations and/or any exceptional emissions from assoc-iated machinery?

4.7 Comment on ambient noise levels and note any existing sources of noise pollution and vibration problems:

a] on the site
b] in the surroundings

4.8 Will tipping operations cause a significant rise in ambient noise levels around the site?

4.9 What measures will be taken to reduce potential noise nuisance?

5.0 Transport

This section to be filled in where disposal site involves off-site access (Note – impact of internal haul roads is assumed to be covered in previous sections). The amount of detail appropriate for comparisons between options in which a transport route is required is dependent upon the type of route and whether it is a new route or involves an increase in existing traffic.

qu.5.2   Information on existing traffic levels should be sought from the Highway Authorities, British Rail or British Waterways Board, as appropriate.

qu.5.4   Frontage to be defined as within about 25m. Estimates can be made as counts, built up distances along the route or proportions of grid squares as appropriate.

qu.5.5   This should include schools, hospitals, public assembly halls, recreation areas.

qu.5.6   Assess effects of noise, dust, vibration, mud, visual intrusion, etc.

qu.5.7   Consider accident risks to cyclists and pedestrians, delays to other traffic, implications at rail level crossings, etc.

qu.5.10   As for question 5.6

ENVIRONMENTAL ASSESSMENT – cont'd

5.0 Transport

a] Use of Existing Transport
    Route

5.1 Note length and type of
     route to be used

5.2 What level of increase
     on existing traffic
     along the route would
     be involved?

5.3 Will there be an
     increased use of the
     route at night?

5.4 Estimate the number of
     residential properties
     along the frontage of
     the route and within
     ½km of loading/unloading
     points

5.5 Note other sensitive
     properties in same
     locations

5.6 Assess how seriously
     these will be affected
     by increased traffic

5.7 Will spoil transport
     cause conflict with
     other traffic movements
     at access points or
     along the route?

b] Use of New Transport
    Route

5.8 What level of usage
     would be involved?

5.9 What land would be
     taken for the new route
     (give existing uses
     and areas)?

5.10 Assess the type and
     severity of any impact
     caused by the new
     route

qu.6.1   Note for example any impacts on third parties such as risk of
          sea-based disposal blocking sewage outfalls.

qu.6.3   This is intended to demonstrate the flexibility of the site to
          longer term expansion. However, this may not be necessary for some
          schemes.

ENVIRONMENTAL ASSESSMENT - cont'd

6.0 Other

6.1 Note any other adverse
environmental impacts
of the option

6.2 Note any other ameli-
orative change or envir-
onmental gain arising
from the option, e.g.
restoration of GDO tip
sites or other degraded
sites

6.3 What provision is there
for any longer term
extension of the disposal
site?

PHASE II - ENVIRONMENTAL

SUMMARY OF ENVIRONMENTAL IMPACTS

OPTION:

ENVIRONMENTAL FACTOR	DATE/TIMING OF IMPACT	DESCRIPTION AND QUANTIFICATION OF IMPACT	PARTIES AFFECTED
VISUAL			
Property nearest to new tip			
Properties within VEM within ½km of new tip			
Properties within VEM between ½km and 1km of new tip			
Other features within visual envelope			
Views blocked out by new tip			
Intrusiveness of final form and after-use			
LAND USE			
Land take: area/use/grade			
Properties affected on site			
After-use			
ECOLOGICAL, HERITAGE, RECREATIONAL			
Ecological and landscape features			
Heritage features			
Recreational Uses			

PHASE II - ENVIRONMENTAL

SUMMARY OF ENVIRONMENTAL IMPACTS (CONTINUED)

OPTION:

ENVIRONMENTAL FACTOR	DATE/TIMING OF IMPACT	DESCRIPTION AND QUANTIFICATION OF IMPACT	PARTIES AFFECTED
POLLUTANTS			
Water			
Air			
Noise			
TRANSPORT ROUTE			
Length and type of route			
a] Existing Route			
Level of increase in traffic			
Residential areas – along frontage – around loading/ unloading sites			
Other sensitive properties			
Traffic conflict			
b] New Route			
Level of usage			
Land Take			
Impact (visual, noise, dust, etc.)			
OTHER IMPACTS			

PHASE II - ENVIRONMENTAL

OPTION DIFFERENCES

ENVIRONMENTAL FACTOR	Option A	Option B	Are the differences significant?	If so, which option is	
				least affected?	worst affected?
VISUAL Intrusiveness during operational stage					
Intrusiveness of final form					
LAND USE Effects during operational stage					
Effects of after-use					
ECOLOGICAL, HERITAGE, RECREATIONAL					
Ecological and heritage features					
Recreational uses					
POLLUTANTS Water					
Air					
Noise					
TRANSPORT ROUTE					
OTHER					

PHASE III - COMBINED EVALUATION

PHASE III – COMBINED EVALUATION

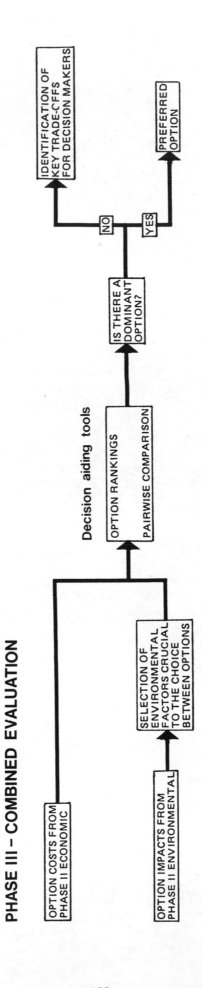

OPTION COSTS FROM PHASE II ECONOMIC

OPTION IMPACTS FROM PHASE II ENVIRONMENTAL

SELECTION OF ENVIRONMENTAL FACTORS CRUCIAL TO THE CHOICE BETWEEN OPTIONS

Decision aiding tools

OPTION RANKINGS

PAIRWISE COMPARISON

IS THERE A DOMINANT OPTION?

NO

YES

IDENTIFICATION OF KEY TRADE-OFFS FOR DECISION MAKERS

PREFERRED OPTION

PHASE III

Statement on Key Environmental Factors

Identify and justify those factors where the differences between options are critical to the decision making. Only these factors are then carried forward for use in the decision aiding tools.

Two decision aiding tools are available to assist users in deciding upon the critical issues between disposal options. These tools can be used in isolation but are better in combination. They can be modified where considered necessary by mutual agreement of the users.

PHASE III

Option Rankings

	Option A	Option B	Etc.
ECONOMIC			
EAC/tonne or /m³			
Initial Cost			
ENVIRONMENTAL			
Visual – Operational			
– Final Form			
Land Use – Operational			
– Final Form			
Ecological and Heritage			
Recreational			
Pollutants – Water			
– Air			
– Noise			
Transport Route			
Other Factors			

METHOD

1. Allocate stars between options on each factor. One star indicates the worst option, five the best with the remainder within this range according to relative performance.

2. Environmental entries are only made where impacts are significantly different between options and judged to be critical to the decision between these options.

3. Compare columns visually but do not sum the stars. Do any options stand out as overwhelmingly better or worse than others?

4. High incidence of stars implies preferred options but all factors have equal importance.

PAIRWISE COMPARISON

	Compare two options and give reasons for preference	Compare winner and next option and give reasons for preference	and so on
ECONOMIC			
EAC/tonne or /m³			
Initial Cost			
ENVIRONMENTAL			
Visual – Operational			
– Final Form			
Land Use – Operational			
– After-use			
Ecological and Heritage			
Recreational			
Pollutants – Water			
– Air			
– Noise			
Transport Route			
Other Factors			

Which Option preferred
overall?

METHOD

1. Compare two options for each factor and give reasons for preference. Order can be random or guided by the results of Option Rankings Summary.
2. Environmental entries are only made where impacts are significantly different between options and judged to be critical to the decision between these options.
3. Compare winner and next option and give reasons for preference and so on.
4. Where a clear preference does not emerge compare the next option with each in turn.
5. When the process is complete, some options will have been eliminated. Check that the first option eliminated has been compared against the front runner to ensure conformity of choice. If not, complete the necessary comparison.
6. For those options not eliminated, identify the final trade-offs to be made by decision makers.

PHASE III

KEY ISSUES STATEMENT

STATEMENT ON PREFERRED DISPOSAL OPTION

Summarise the key trade-offs which need to be resolved between short-listed options by decision makers

or

Justify in brief terms why the preferred option has been chosen with reference to the main environmental effects and the economic costs of the option.

USE OF THE EVALUATIVE FRAMEWORK FOR RECEPTION SITES

This Annex provides guidance on the use of the Evaluative Framework in the assessment of options as sources of colliery spoil for a given reception site. Only the Phase I questionnaire takes a different format to the main Framework and this is included here.

Phase I

(i)   Complete the shortened questionnaire (overleaf) to select feasible options of source collieries, with alternative transport modes.

Phase II

(i)   Estimate the costs of spoil disposal for:

(a)   local tipping at each source colliery;
(b)   remote disposal to the reception site from each source colliery by each transport mode.

(ii)   Summarise the additional costs of using the remote site for each option using the Option Costs summary table.

(iii)   Assess the environmental impacts of:

(a)   local tipping at each source colliery;
(b)   transport route between source colliery and reception site, by each mode of transport (the environmental effects at the reception site need not be included as they should be common to all options).

(iv)   Identify the differences between source options in the Option Differences table, in terms of the benefits gained, impacts avoided, or opportunities lost if spoil were not tipped locally at the colliery.

(v)   Identify the differences between the feasible transport options to the reception site, in terms of impact upon the environment, other traffic and any benefits arising from greater use of a particular route.

Phase III

(i)   The combined evaluation will compare source options to assist in choosing a preferred source for the reception site.

(ii)   A combined evaluation may also be appropriate to help identify the preferred mode of transport to the reception site.

PHASE I - SELECTION OF OPTIONS AS SOURCES OF COLLIERY SPOIL

TASK 1.　IDENTIFY REQUIREMENTS FOR SPOIL

1.1　What overall quantity of spoil
　　　is required?

1.2　What type/quantities of spoil
　　　could be accommodated
　　　per annum?

　　　　　　　Coarse
　　　　　　　Fines (specify in
　　　　　　　　　　what form)

Output Task 1 -

Define annual quantity of
spoil required at the
reception site:

TASK 2.　DEFINE HANDLING OPTIONS

2.1　What means of access are
　　　available at the reception
　　　site e.g. road, rail, water?

　　　　　(List modes and
　　　　　capacities, e.g.
　　　　　trains/day, maximum
　　　　　barge size.)

2.2　What scale of transport would
　　　be required to carry the
　　　daily volume of spoil and is
　　　it compatible with qu.2.1?

Output Task 2 -

Define preliminary handling
options:

TASK 3. DEFINE OPTIONS OF SOURCE LOCATIONS

3.1   List any collieries within
a feasible range along any
main transport corridors.

(List sites and give spoil
production quantities.)

3.2   Is the quantity of spoil
produced from any of these
collieries sufficient to meet
the tipping requirement?

Yes

No

3.3   If there are insufficient
quantities, can the output
of any collieries be
combined to produce a more
viable scheme?

Yes

If so – which?

No

3.4   Has the suitability of
the source material
been checked?

Output Task 3 –

Define preliminary source
options (with reasons):

TASK 4.   MATCH PRELIMINARY LOCATIONAL AND HANDLING OPTIONS

4.1   Are the source options
located within the
distance threshold
of available transport
modes?

      Yes

If no, dismiss option.

4.2   Will the intended transport
modes and routes cause undue
environmental disturbance
(e.g. excessive number of
lorries)?

If yes, dismiss option.

      No

Output Task 4 -

Define feasible source options.

TASK 5.   WORK UP PRELIMINARY DESIGN AND COSTINGS FOR EACH FEASIBLE OPTION

5.1   Discard any totally
        unrealistic options on
        cost grounds if agreeable
        to all parties.

5.2   Outline the main elements
        of each option, including
        new infrastructure works
        and transport route, and
        approximate phasing
        timetable.

FULL DERIVATION OF THE EAC FORMULA

The full derivation of the Equivalent Annual Cost per tonne (or cubic metre) of spoil is as follows:

$$NPC = \frac{EAC^c \times t_m}{(1+i)^m} + \frac{EAC^c \times t_{(m+1)}}{(1+i)^{m+1}} + \cdots + \frac{EAC^c \times t_n}{(1+i)^n}$$

where

NPC	=	Net Present Cost at year prior to first expenditure (Year O)
EAC^c	=	Equivalent Annual Cost per tonne
t	=	tonnes tipped in year
m	=	year number of first year of tipping
n	=	year number of last year of tipping
i	=	interest rate

As EAC^c is a constant, the above can be rearranged as:

$$NPC = EAC^c \times \sum_{k=m}^{n} \left[\frac{t_k}{(1+i)^k} \right]$$

$$\therefore \quad EAC^c = \frac{NPC}{\sum\limits_{k=m}^{n} \left[\dfrac{t_k}{(1+i)^k} \right]}$$

This is the underlying formula used in the model. Note that if t_k is constant, i.e. the same tonnage is tipped each year, then

$$EAC^c = \frac{NPC}{t \times \sum\limits_{k=m}^{n} \left[\dfrac{1}{(1+i)^k} \right]}$$

Therefore, $EAC^c \times t = \dfrac{NPC}{\sum\limits_{k=m}^{n} \left[\dfrac{1}{(1 + i)^k} \right]}$

The expression on the left is the EAC. The expression on the right reduces to

$$\frac{NPC \times (1 + i)^{m-1} \times i}{1 - \dfrac{1}{(1 + i)^{n - m + 1}}}$$

$m - 1$ is the number of years before tipping commences. $n - m + 1$ is the number of years of tipping. Therefore, in the case where t_k is constant, the above formula reduces to that shown in the main text.

WORKED EXAMPLES OF THE PHASE II ECONOMIC AND ENVIRONMENTAL
SUMMARY TABLES AND THE PHASE III DECISION AIDING TOOLS

The following tables are enclosed to illustrate the techniques included
in the Evaluative Framework. The data represents a reformatting of
information already published to accord with the Framework and no signif-
icance should be attached to the values shown for any of the options.
They are purely illustrative.

PHASE II – ECONOMIC
Summary of Option Costs

	Option A Local £	Option B Rail £	Option C Rail £	Option D Rail £	Option E Road £
Equivalent Annual Cost Per Tonne of Spoil	£1.30	£9.00	£5.80	£4.72	£3.10
Amounting over 20 years to total cost	(£14m)	(£99m)	(£64m)	(£52m)	(£34m)
EACs by activity					
– Acquisition	0.06	0.007	0.007	0.007	0.009
– Preparation	0.17	0.04	0.03	0.03	0.07
– Treatment	–	–	–	–	–
– Handling & Transport	0.58	8.61	5.31	4.42	2.62
– Placement & Compaction	0.42	0.28	0.37	0.36	0.29
– Restoration & Aftercare	0.08	0.04	0.07	0.11	0.08
– Other Costs	0.002	–	–	–	–
– Revenues	–0.009	–	–	–0.18	–
Initial Cost in £'000s	3250	5495	7080	6345	3600

Note: Costs per tonne, instead of per cubic metre, used for consistency with published information.

137

PHASE II - ENVIRONMENTAL

Summary of option differences

ENVIRONMENTAL FACTOR	Option A Local	Option B Rail	Option C Rail	Option D Rail	Option E Road	Are the differences significant?	If so, which option is least affected?	worst affected?
VISUAL								
Intrusiveness during operational stage	new tip above ground level, visible from villages and an A road	filling in void, viewed from 20 houses	filling in void, viewed from 15 houses and an A road	filling in void distant views from Yaxley Village. Views from rail and road	filling in quarry; void, some views from village	YES	B	A
Intrusiveness of final form	new land form but in valley topography	slight increase in levels	slight slopes; grassland with forestry	reclaimed site suitable for new development	former contours to be achieved	YES	C	A
LAND USE								
1. Land use operational stages	use of farmland (33 hectares)	disused chalk pit	disused clay pit	disused pit (already contains pfa)	within active quarry	YES	-	A
After-use	restored to agriculture	possible use for recreation	grassland and forestry	potential development site	agriculture and grassland	YES	D	-
2. Ecological and landscape features	loss of valley contours	loss of water feature	loss of small water feature	-	SSSI in quarry	YES	D	E
3. Heritage features	next to a medieval village site	-	-	-	-	NO	-	-
4. Recreational uses	-	-	-	-	-	NO	-	-
POLLUTANTS								
Water	diversion of valley stream and local drainage	effects upon local drainage (chalk base)	changes to local drainage systems (clay base)	slight risk for river and local water courses (clay base)	risk to nearby reservoir (limestone base)	NO	-	-
Air	-	dust may affect orchards	-	dust pollution	conflict with limestone	YES	-	B
Noise	dwellings affected by vehicle noise on high tip	disturbance in quiet locality	-	-	active quarry already with noise	YES	E	B
TRANSPORT ROUTE	local tipping with on-site conveyor	200km through cities	100km use of local line	60km use of main line	37 or 58km through towns and villages	YES	A	E
		(-------2 or 3 trains per day-------)			(95 lorry loads per day)			
OTHER								
Long term capacity	extension feasible	other pits available	other sites but new rail head required	extension of conveyor	new voids in same quarry	YES	-	C

138

PHASE III

Environmental Factors

Statement on Importance of Environmental Factors

For the purposes of Phase III, only the most important factors are taken forward.

In the Summary of Option Differences no significant differences between options were identified in terms of Heritage Features, Recreational Uses and Water Pollutants. These three environmental factors were therefore not considered further. Of the other factors (all of which showed significant differences between options), it was decided that the following 4 factors were less important than others for this particular testing of options :

(i)   Visual – Final Form : each option would result in restored or partly restored site, either a filled-in void or valley, with impacts of less importance than the visual impact during operational stages.

(ii)   Ecological and Landscape Features : although there would be impacts on a current SSSI and on water features the effects and differences between options were regarded as not so important as the impact on land use.

(iii)   Air Pollution : although the differences between options were regarded as significant the impacts were not judged to be as important as the differences in noise impacts.

(iv)   Long Term Capacity : each option has the possiblity of further capacity with relatively minor changes, and therefore this factor was omitted from the final evaluation.

NOTE: Although this step has been made of taking forward to Phase III those environmental factors in which there are significant differences between options as well as being judged as being of major importance, it must be remembered that the evaluation is concerned with the marginal differences between options, not the absolute impact of disposing of colliery spoil.

139

PHASE III

Option Rankings

	Option A Local	Option B Rail	Option C Rail	Option D Rail	Option E Road
ECONOMIC					
Equivalent Annual Cost per Tonne of Spoil	*****	*	**	***	****
Initial Cost	*****	***	*	**	*****
ENVIRONMENTAL					
Visual – Operational – Final Form	*	*****	***	****	****
Land Use – Operational	*	*****	*****	****	****
– After Use	*	***	****	*****	****
Ecological and Landscape					
Heritage					
Recreational					
Pollutants – Water – Air – Noise	**	*	****	****	*****
Transport Route	*****	**	***	****	*
Other Factors Long Term Capacity					

METHOD

1. Allocate stars between options on each factor. One star indicates the worst option, five the best with the remainder within this range according to relative performance.

2. Environmental entries are only made where impacts are significantly different between options and judged to be critical to the decision between these options.

3. Compare columns visually but do not sum stars. Do any options stand out as overwhelmingly better or worse than others.

4. High incidence of stars implies preferred options but all factors have equal importance.

Pairwise Comparison

	Options A Local & B Rail	Options A Local & C Rail	Options A Local & D Rail	Options C Rail & D Rail	Options A Local & E Road	Options D Rail & E Road
ECONOMIC						
Equivalent Annual Cost per Tonne of Spoil	A – £7.70/t cheaper amounting to £85M over 20 years	A – £4.50/t cheaper amounting to £50M over 20 years	A – £3.42/t cheaper amounting to £38M over 20 years	A – £1.08/t cheaper amounting to £12M over 20 years	D – £1.80/t cheaper amounting to £20M over 20 years	E – £1.62/t cheaper amounting to £18M over 20 years
Initial Cost	A – £2.25M cheaper	A – £3.8M cheaper	A – £3.1M cheaper	D – £0.7M cheaper	A – £0.35M cheaper	E – £2.7M cheaper
ENVIRONMENTAL						
Visual – Operational	B – tipping into a void is preferable to above ground, fewer houses close by	C – tipping into a void is preferable to above ground	D – tipping into a void is preferable to above ground	D – both in voids, fewer houses close by	E – tipping into a void is preferable to above ground	= – both in voids
– Final Form						
Land Use – Operational	B – no loss of agricultural land	C – no loss of agricultural land	D – no loss of agricultural land	C – no conflict with current land uses	E – no loss of agricultural land	= – both have existing uses but unlikely to be much affected
– After-use	B – recreation facilities in short supply in area	C – returned to grassland from derelict site	D – development site potential	D – development site potential	E – return to grassland from derelict site	D – development site potential
Ecological and Landscape						
Heritage						
Recreational						
Pollutants – Water						
– Air						
– Noise	= – void shields noise creation at C but more noticeable in rural area	C – void shields noise creation Radial spreader quieter	D – void shields noise creation Radial spreader quieter	= – both in voids	E – void shields noise creation Radial spreader quieter	E – additional noise at quarry less noticeable than in area of CEGB operations
Transport Route	A – no off-site transport	A' – no off-site transport	A – no off-site transport	D – main line rail and shorter route	A – no off-site transport	D – rail less disturbing than road through villages
Other Factors Long term capacity						
Which Option preferred overall?	A – extra cost to go to B is huge in relation to operational and after-use advantages	? Is it worth £50M to create grassland and protect agricultural land?	? Is it worth £38M to create possible development land and protect agricultural land?	D – cheaper and greater environmental advantages conflicts with CEGB not serious	? Is it worth £20M to create grassland and protect agricultural land?	? Is it worth £18M to create less disturbance by rail and possible development gain?
	B – dismissed	Difficult trade-off	Difficult trade-off	C – dismissed	Difficult trade-off	Difficult trade-off

METHOD
1. Compare two options for each factor and give reasons for preference. Order can be random or guided by the results of Options Ranking Summary.
2. Environmental entries are only made where impacts are significantly different between options and judged to be critical to the decision between these options.
3. Compare winner and next option and give reasons for preference and so on.
4. Where a clear preference does not emerge compare the next option with each in turn.
5. When the process is complete, some options will have been eliminated. Check that the first option has been compared against the front runner to ensure conformity of choice. If not, complete the necessary comparison.
6. For those options not eliminated, identify the final trade-offs to be made by decision makers.

PHASE III

KEY ISSUES STATEMENT

Option A Local v Option E Road v Option D Rail

1.   Is it worth spending £20M extra to transport spoil to Option E or £38M extra to Option D in order:

   (i)   to avoid taking agricultural land at Option A; and
   (ii) to create a positive use from derelict land at either
                               remote site?

2.   If a remote site is preferred, is it worth spending the extra £18M to get the environmental advantages of rail transport in order:

   (i)   to avoid nearly 100 heavy lorries (in each direction) each day through villages en route to Option E;   and

   (ii) to create possible development land on the edge of a New Town under Option D?

Printed for Her Majesty's Stationery Office by Hobbs the Printers of Southampton
(2737/86) Dd240335 C17 10/86 G3379